THRILLING
Comprehension

Support material for use with
Five and Ten Minute Thrillers

MICHAEL COLEMAN

Thrilling Comprehension
Ref 05001
ISBN 1 85503 228 7

© Text: Michael Coleman
© Illustration: Meena Arnold
All rights reserved
First published 1996

LDA, Duke Street, Wisbech, Cambs PE13 2AE

Contents

Flight 901
by B Jackson and S Quintanilla

Summary

Sam has been sacked from his job with an airline. In revenge, he is going to blow up one of their planes – flight 901. His suitcase has got a bomb in it. He plans to have his case loaded on to the plane, then run away. As he waits, he talks to a little girl. She tells Sam that she is going on the flight. At the last minute Sam rushes out with his bag to an open field. There's a huge explosion . . .

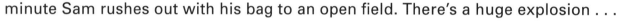

Questions

1) What was Sam going to do at 8.15?
2) When does Sam expect the bomb to 'explode'?
3) Can you think of another word, or words, for explode?
4) What is the name of the girl Sam starts talking to?
5) What does her rag doll make Sam remember?
6) How does he get out to the runway quickly?
7) Why do you think Sam went to an open field?
8) Do you think Sam is a good man or a bad man?

Things to think about

- Sam's plan is in the form of a timetable. Write it out as one.
  What other timetables can you think of?

- Why do you think Sam changes his mind? Write down two reasons.

- What do you think happens to Sam at the end of this story?
  Write another few sentences to tell us.

© LDA Thrilling Comprehension

Someone at the Door
by B Jackson and S Quintanilla

Summary

Karen and Paula are trying to fix a new lock on the door. A young man turns up. He says he's calling on people to see if they'd like to buy the newspaper he works for. He helps them fix the lock and says he'll come back another time to talk about the newspaper. Some days later, Paula rings to say that the killer is posing as a newspaper salesman. But Karen is already opening the door . . .

Questions

1) On whose door are Karen and Paula trying to fit a new lock?
2) Why are they fitting the lock?
3) How does the young man know how to fit the lock?
4) How long does it take the man to fit the lock?
5) What suggestion does the young man make? Does Karen agree?
6) When Paula rings Karen two days later, what does she want Karen to do?
7) What makes you think Paula's warning has come too late?

Things to think about

- Does the story say that the young man is the killer?
- Do you think he is? Why or why not?
- Write a few sentences to say what happens next.

The Playmate
by B Jackson and S Quintanilla

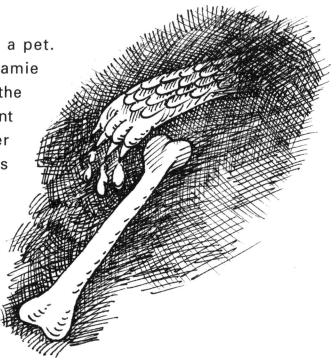

Summary

Jamie's mother won't let him have a pet. But what she doesn't know is that Jamie already has one. It's a creature from the river and it lives in the flooded basement of an empty building. Jamie calls her Sharon. When a boy disappears on his way home from school, Jamie's mother worries about the time he spends out on the streets. She says he can bring his pet home. What neither she nor Jamie know is that Sharon eats humans . . .

 Questions

1) Why doesn't Jamie's mother want him to have a pet?
2) Describe the building Jamie plays in.
3) How do you know it is near the river?
4) Sharon slithers when she moves. Can you think of another word for 'slither'?
5) What does Sharon drop from her mouth?
6) How does Jamie persuade his Mum that he needs a playmate?
7) What sort of pet does she think Sharon is?

Things to think about

- Write down the words used to describe Sharon. Why do you think Jamie thought he had never seen anything so beautiful?
- We are told on page 9 about a boy who disappeared on his way home from school. Write a story about what happened to him.
- What do you think happens when Jamie brings Sharon home? Write a story that carries on from where The Playmate ends.

A Matter of Time
by B Jackson and S Quintanilla

Summary

Mr Stewart visits the doctor. He has a strange tale to tell. He is 252 years old, and fed up with living. He wants to die. Can the doctor give him something to help him kill himself? So the doctor writes a prescription . . .

Questions

1) When does Mr Stewart think he was born?
2) Does the doctor believe him?
3) What does Mr Stewart say he noticed about his friends?
4) How many times does Mr Stewart say he's been married?
5) What has just happened to Mr Stewart's latest wife?
6) What does Mr Stewart ask the doctor to do for him?
7) What does the doctor actually do?

Things to think about

- On page 5 there's a description of a battlefield. Which sentences make the scene sound peaceful? Can you think of some different sentences?
- If you were really 252 years old, how would you try to make others believe you? Write a letter to do this.
- Would you like to be that old? Why or why not? Write down some reasons for your answer.

The Arsonist
by B Jackson and S Quintanilla

Summary

Nobody wants the Fry building. Mr Fry pays Sheila £50,000 to set fire to it so that he can collect the insurance money. Sheila does her job well. Soon the building is on fire and fire engines are racing from all over the city to try to put it out. Sheila drives home only to find her own house is on fire! There's no chance of putting the fire out. All the fire engines in the area are busy at another blaze . . .

Questions

1) Where does Mr Fry meet Sheila?
2) What does the word arson mean?
3) How does Sheila start the fire in the Fry building?
4) What does she do after starting the fire?
5) When Sheila gets home, she can tell something is wrong. How?
6) What is Sheila's neighbour trying to do?
7) What is inside the house that is really important to her?

Things to think about

- On page 5 the author describes the fire starting. Write a totally different description of a fire dying down as the fire fighters put it out.

- Do you think Sheila got what she deserved? Were you pleased with how the story ended? Why or why not?

- An arsonist is the name given to a person who carries out the act of arson. Can you think of other words ending in -ist which are made in the same way? (Clue: how about somebody who looks after teeth?)

© **LDA** Thrilling Comprehension

The Hitchhiker
by B Jackson and S Quintanilla

Summary

Paula is driving down a lonely road. As she drives she remembers what her dead father told her: 'Never give a lift to a stranger.' But when she passes a woman hitchhiker she stops. The woman goes to sleep. Paula puts on the radio and hears about a dangerous woman murderer the police are looking for. Paula takes out the gun she keeps in the car. She points it at the sleeping hitchhiker. Just as she's about to pull the trigger, something happens to make her change her mind.

Questions

1) Why doesn't Paula usually enjoy the drive between Carrington and Polton?
2) What did Paula always tease her father about?
3) Why does she pick up the hitchhiker?
4) What does Paula think after she hears the first news report?
5) Where was her gun?
6) What makes Paula change her mind?
7) What does she do with the gun?

Things to think about

- The road Paula takes is described at the start of the book. How do you think it makes the road sound? Write a description of the road where you live.
- On page 3 there is a saying: making mountains out of molehills. What does it mean? Can you think of any other well known sayings?
- Do you think hitchhiking is dangerous? Write down some reasons why or why not.

A Time to Remember
by B Jackson and S Quintanilla

Summary

A man in shabby clothes goes to the police station. He says he can't remember who he is. The sergeant sends him to a mission for homeless people run byMike. The man decides he wants to be known as James. After a while James begins to remember odd things about himself. Then, one day, he doesn't come back to the mission. Mike goes to the police. They have just found out that James is a killer who has escaped from a hospital. He loses his memory whenever he murders somebody. Then, when his memory starts to return, he wants to kill again. Mike has had a lucky escape. Meanwhile, James has met a doctor who's an expert at helping people get their memories back . . .

Questions

1) Why is the man in the story glad to be in the police station?
2) What happened to the man just before Mike found him?
3) What does Mike see about James that's different to the other people who come to the mission?
4) What is the first thing James remembers?
5) How does this memory make James feel?
6) What is wrong with James?
7) Why is the doctor James is seeing in danger?

 ## Things to think about

- What is a mission? (page 4) Look it up in a dictionary. Do you think it's a good word to describe Mike's place?
- This story is about memories. What is your earliest memory? Write about it.
- What do you think will happen if the doctor does help James to get his memory back?

Chon
by B Jackson and S Quintanilla

Summary

Mary hasn't got much money. She is waiting for the bus to go to work. Suddenly, a green spaceship lands in front of her! A woman comes out saying she has gold for somebody called Chon. Mary says she isn't Chon, and the ship goes away. Soon after, another ship comes. This one has more gifts for Chon.

It goes away too when Mary says that she isn't the person they're looking for. But Mary starts thinking. When the bus finally comes, she waves it past. Instead, she waits for the next spaceship to land . . .

Questions

1) Why does Mary live in the country?
2) What would she really like to do today?
3) Mary watches as something lands. What does she think it is at first?
4) When it does land, what does it look like?
5) What gift is the second visitor carrying?
6) How is the third ship different to the first two?
7) Why does Mary say she is Chon?

Things to think about

- In the story, we're not told what the lizard ships are. What do you think they are? Where do you think they come from? Describe this place.
- Who do you think Chon is and what is she doing on Earth?
- What do you think the two boxes contain? Write the next part of this story.

Friday Afternoon
by B Jackson and S Quintanilla

Summary

Dean's bus is stuck in a traffic jam. Nobody knows what's happening. And then Dean hears on his personal stereo that the country is being attacked by missiles. There is nothing he can do. All around him people are in a panic. But Dean can only sit and think about his father, and how ungrateful he'd been to him the last time they met. Outside, a large glow is getting brighter and brighter . . .

Questions

1) What is Dean travelling in?
2) There is a traffic jam. The traffic is said to be bumper-to-bumper. What does this mean? Think of another way of saying this.
3) Why is Dean the only one on the bus who knows what is happening?
4) What does he realise is going to happen?
5) Why does he think of his father?
6) What are Dean's last words?
7) What is the 'huge companion' to the sun?

Things to think about

- Dean isn't the only one who hears the terrible news. Give two examples from the book showing how different people behave.
- What do you think Dean's father would have said to Dean if he'd known what his son's last thought was?
- What would you do if you suddenly heard that you only had a few minutes to live?

Princess
by B Jackson and S Quintanilla

Summary

A thief breaks into an old couple's house. He makes them bring out all their money but it's not very much. Then he hears a loud thumping sound coming from behind a locked door. The couple tell the thief that it's their small dog, Princess. They warn him not to open the door. But he does . . .

Questions

1) How does the thief get into the house?
2) What does he think he could get £100 for?
3) What breed of dog does the old man say Princess is?
4) What does Gladys give to the thief?
5) There are clues in the story to show that Princess isn't just a little dog. Give two of these clues.
6) What does the thief think must be in the room with Princess?
7) What happens to him?

Things to think about

- What do you think Princess really looks like? Describe her.
- The old couple say that the thief deserved what he got. Do you agree?
- Imagine that there's something behind a door that only you know about. Describe the noises it makes. See if anybody can guess what it is!

The Birthday Present
by B Jackson and S Quintanilla

Summary

John has no job. On his birthday, he treats himself to a pizza. While he's eating it, he sees a woman whose car has a flat tyre. Nobody will help her. John goes out and changes the tyre for her. The woman says that in return she can grant John one wish. He doesn't really believe her. But when he gets home the phone rings . . .

Questions

1) Why does John feel a bit guilty about buying the pizza?
2) Describe two things about the woman's car that tell us it is old.
3) What do the woman's eyes remind John of?
4) What does the woman say she can give to John?
5) Why does John's wife come home early?
6) How does this make John feel?
7) What good news do they get over the phone?

Things to think about

- On page 3, the woman is described as ageless. What does this mean?
- If you were given one wish, what would you wish for? Why?
- Many stories have a message. What message has this story got?

© **LDA** Thrilling Comprehension

The Blue Club
by B Jackson and S Quintanilla

Summary

Rodney is acting as a hypnotist. He performs at The Blue Club. One evening he calls a man up from the audience and hypnotises him. He asks the man to describe his earliest memory. The man goes on to talk about getting ready to invade the Earth. He's an alien! Rodney sends him back to the audience, but remembers his face. He plans to kill him, and all those like him.

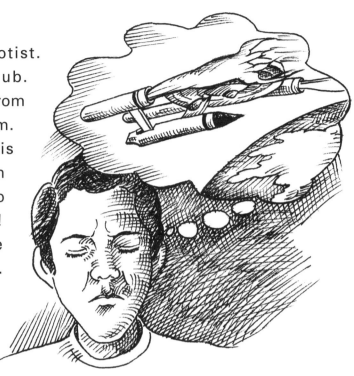

Questions

1) What sort of people like to go to The Blue Club?
2) Why did Rodney first decide to go to The Blue Club?
3) What are the names of the two men Rodney invites on to the stage?
4) What is the second man's earliest memory?
5) What does Rodney do to wake them up?
6) What does Val do at the end of the show?
7) Rodney plans to eliminate the man. Think of another word for eliminate.

Things to think about

- If you were a hypnotist, what would you get someone to do? Write a description of the scene.
- Who or what do you think Val is?
- If you went to another planet, what do you think some of the problems would be?

The Everett Eyes
by B Jackson and S Quintanilla

Summary

A strange thing has happened to Cameron Everett. His eyes have begun to glow. His father is called to school by the head teacher, Mr Fowler. That is when Mr Everett explains that this happens to all the men in their family just before they're eighteen. It only lasts a month. Mr Fowler says that Cameron must stay away from school until he returns to normal. Cameron doesn't want to, but nothing will change Mr Fowler's mind. As they leave the school Mr Fowler starts to scream. There is another power that comes to all Everetts when their eyes glow . . .

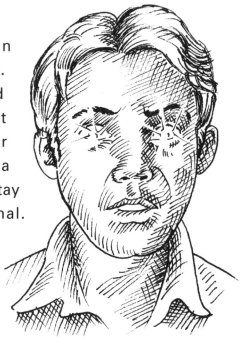

Questions

1) How does Cameron feel as he waits to see Mr Fowler?
2) What lesson was Cameron in when his eyes started to glow?
3) What are some of the pupils saying about Cameron?
4) Cameron's father explains that all men in the Everett family get glowing eyes. How long does it last?
5) Why doesn't Cameron want to stay away from school?
6) What does Mr Fowler do at the end of the story?
7) Who has made it happen? How?

 Things to think about

- Would you have sent Cameron home if you were Mr Fowler? Why or why not?
- Imagine that you can make things happen just by thinking about them. Describe one thing that you would make happen.
- The 'Everett Eyes' are hereditary – that is, it is something passed on from a parent to a child. Can you think of anything that's hereditary in your family?

The Fancy Dress Party
by B Jackson and S Quintanilla

Summary

Mike Kane has been invited to a party. When he arrives, everybody is in fancy dress. Mike is met by somebody dressed as the devil. He introduces Mike to a man named Phil. Mike discovers that he was at school with Phil. Mike got Phil expelled from school. Trying to get away, Mike meets Margaret. He was going to marry her, then married another woman. In fact, everybody at the party is a person Mike has hurt in some way. Mike tries to leave, but his host stops him. Only then does Mike realise that the devil isn't in fancy dress . . .

 **Questions**

1) Where is the party being held?
2) What sort of party is it?
3) Why does Mike feel awkward when he arrives?
4) Who is the host of the party?
5) Why was Phil expelled from school?
6) How did Mike hurt Margaret's feelings?
7) Mike is told that the guests at the party have come to 'collect their debts'. What does this mean? Think of any other word or words that mean debt.

 Things to think about

- If you were invited to a fancy dress party, who would you go as? Why?
- The story is about Mike finding out how bad he's been in his life. Describe him as a person.
- What do you think happens next? Will Mike be any different when he's allowed to leave the party?

The Look-Alike
by B Jackson and S Quintanilla

Summary

Bill Martin looks just like a famous pop star. At first Bill likes being mistaken for someone famous, but he soon gets fed up with it. One day, he's in a steak bar when a girl asks for his autograph. Rather than argue, he signs. He continues to act like the pop star. But it gets him into trouble. Outside, a man with a gun comes up to him. He says Ron Love owes his boss £150,000. Bill says he isn't Ron Love, but the gunman won't believe him . . .

Questions

1) Who does Bill look like?
2) What were the newspapers saying about Ron Love?
3) What is Bill asked to sign in the steak bar?
4) Who gives him a pen to use?
5) Why does Bill leave the steak bar?
6) Who comes up to Bill outside?
7) Why doesn't he believe what Bill tells him?

 ### Things to think about

- Would it be good to look like somebody famous? Why or why not?
- At the end of the story, the man with the gun doesn't believe Bill. What else do you think Bill could say to make the man believe that he isn't Ron Love?
- Can you always believe what you read in the newspapers? Look at the same story in two newspapers and check for differences.

The Specialist
by B Jackson and S Quintanilla

Summary

Van pays a visit to Dr A Lucard. Van's friend says he's a specialist. But there's something strange about the doctor's waiting room. The other patient in there looks very pale and has large teeth, like a vampire's. So, too, does the girl receptionist! But they can't be vampires, can they? Everyone knows that vampires don't come out during the day. Van goes in to see the doctor, and tells him what he thinks . . .

Questions

1) What is the name of Van's friend?
2) What is the name of the doctor that Van goes to see?
3) Two other people are in the waiting room. Who are they?
4) They look the same in one way. What is it?
5) What does Van notice about the doctor's hand?
6) What does Van tell the doctor he thinks about the people outside?
7) Do you think the doctor's smile is a friendly one? Why or why not?

Things to think about

- There are a number of clues in the story to show that all the people at the doctor's are vampires. What are they?
- Write about what happens next in the story. Make it into a surprise – for instance, what if Van was wearing a cross and chain under his shirt?
- The doctor's name is A Lucard, which is 'dracula' spelt backwards. What do you get if you write your name backwards. Could it be turned into another name?

Grounds for Suspicion
by Michael Coleman

Summary

Tessa Bray wants to write crime stories. She is always looking for ideas. When she goes with her mother to look at a cottage she meets Mr Stone, the owner. He seems very nervous and Mrs Stone is nowhere to be seen. When she thinks about other 'clues' she's seen in the cottage, Tessa decides that something odd is going on! She sneaks back for another look. There she meets Mr Farthing, the estate agent, who explains everything. Or does he?

Questions

1) What is the name of the cottage Tessa and her mother go to visit?
2) What are the three book titles Tessa makes up?
3) Describe Mr Stone.
4) What does she think Mr Stone might have done?
5) What does Tessa see in Mr Stone's garden?
6) How does Mr Farthing explain what has happened?
7) What does Tessa fail to spot? Would it have shown she was right after all?

Things to think about

- Tessa made up a book title from the name of Mr Stone's cottage. Can you make up some mystery book titles from the name of your school?
- Keep your eyes open! Tessa spotted things around her. Write down five things you can see from where you're sitting – especially anything odd!
- Make up a story about one of the things on your list.

© **LDA** Thrilling Comprehension

I Dare You
by Helen McCann

Summary

Tim and Pete want to join the Gang.
To do so, they have to accept a dare.
This is to bring back something from an
empty old house at the edge of a cliff.
Not only is the house in a dangerous
condition, it's supposed to be haunted.
Tim and Pete accept the dare. They go into
an upstairs room – and are scared by a
terrible sight. As they run from the house
Pete slips over the edge of the cliff. It looks
as if he will fall onto the rocks below.
Suddenly, from nowhere, a man with a rope
arrives to rescue him. The two boys think he must be
the man who scared them. But as they watch him go into
the house, a tramp comes out – and tells them he was alone and saw nobody . . .

Questions

1) Who are the main characters in this story?
2) What does the sign outside Cliff House say?
3) The man who used to live in Cliff House was a hermit. Think of another word for hermit.
4) Why is the house dangerous?
5) The boys find the shell in a bedroom. But what else do they think they find in the same room?
6) What is it about the man who rescues Pete that makes him sound good?
7) What was strange about him? Why?

Things to think about

- Would you have taken the dare and gone to Cliff House? Why or why not?
- How would this story need to be changed if it was set in a town?
- Do you believe in ghosts? Write down two reasons why you do, or you don't.

Dead Lucky
by Sue Welford

Summary

Marion is trapped in a hotel by a snowstorm. There is only one other guest. His name is Peter. They have dinner together and become good friends. At the end of the evening a policeman arrives in a Land Rover. He tells them about a killer known as 'The Tiger' who has just murdered the fourteenth victim. The body was found nearby. That night, Marion can't sleep for thinking about the murder. Suddenly, there's a knock at her door. It's Peter . . .

Questions

1) Describe the man behind the desk. Does he sound sinister?
2) What is Marion like? Does she sound sinister?
3) Outside the hotel is a 'desert of white snow'. Can you think of another word instead of desert?
4) Why is the serial killer known as 'The Tiger'?
5) What is Peter like? Does he sound sinister?
6) What is Marion especially proud of? Can you find another place in the book which shows this?
7) So who is the serial killer, Marion or Peter? Why?

 ### Things to think about

- In this book, the serial killer has a nickname which tells you something about him/her. What nicknames do you know? (Your teacher's, maybe!) Why do they have that nickname?
- The story ends without saying who the killer really is. Write the next page.
- The newspapers often give real murderers nicknames like 'The Black Panther' and 'The Yorkshire Ripper'. Do you think this is a good thing? Why or why not?

© **LDA** Thrilling Comprehension

Knockdown Row
by Flora Stewart

Summary

Mrs Devlin is an old woman who lives in a house which is due to be knocked down. People say she has lots of money hidden there somewhere. Nick tricks his way in by pretending to be Mrs Devlin's long-lost son. When she catches him nosing around, they have an argument and Mrs Devlin falls down the stairs. Thinking she's dead, Nick leaves her. He finds the hidden money in a cupboard – but before he can get out the heavy wooden door slams shut. As time goes by, he gets weaker and weaker. When Mrs Devlin is found alive and taken to hospital, nobody knows Nick is there. And then the house starts shaking . . .

Questions

1) What is the real name for Knockdown Row?
2) Nick thinks that Mrs Devlin has a lot of money stashed away. Think of another word for 'stashed'.
3) There is a photo on the wall. Where was it taken?
4) What does Nick see that tells him Mrs Devlin will soon be leaving her house?
5) What does Nick think has happened to Mrs Devlin when she falls down the stairs? Does he care?
6) Why can't Nick escape from the cupboard?
7) What will happen to him?

Things to think about

- Do you feel sorry for Nick? Explain why you do or why you don't.
- If you had to hide some money in a house, where would you choose?
- What do you think it's like being old? Describe an old person you know and say whether he or she is happy or sad.

Monkey Business
by Sue Welford

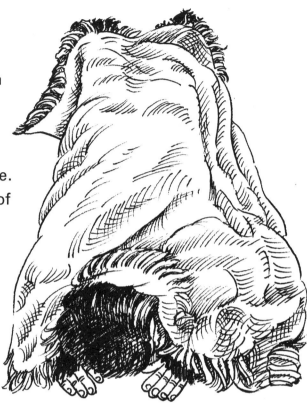

Summary

Tracy and her father set out to deliver a birthday cake to a party. But their car breaks down and they have to go to a garage. Setting off again, Tracy's father stops to help a man who's got a flat tyre. He's also got something on the back seat of his car – something hidden under a blanket. Could it be a kidnap victim, just like in the film Tracy had seen earlier? When a police car arrives, the truth comes out!

 Questions

1) Who are Tracy and her dad trying to find, and where does she live?
2) What happened to the girl in the film Tracy had been watching before they left?
3) Tracy and her dad get lost in the countryside. What words tell you that it was dark and spooky?
4) What does Tracy see when she looks inside the man's car? Why does it remind her of the film she was watching?
5) What trick does she use to speak to her father on his own?
6) How does Tracy's dad get help?
7) What has the man really got in the back of his car?

✏️ *Things to think about*

- On page 19, what words are used to make the man sound evil? Make up another description of him that would make him sound even worse!
- Have you ever been lost? Describe how it felt.
- Write a story about what happened when the next-door neighbour saw you trying out your costume for a fancy dress party in the back garden!

Neep-Heid
by Frances Hendry

Summary

Alison is in the back of her father's trailer. They're heading home when they spot some thieves stealing sheep from a farm. Alison's father is captured, but the thieves don't realise she's there. She waits until they've loaded the sheep and are about to escape with her father as hostage. She then undoes the back of their truck. The sheep get out and the thieves are forced to stop. In the darkness, Alison does one more thing before running off and calling the police. Never again will her father be able to call her neep-heid.

Questions

1) What does neep-heid mean?
2) What favour have they done for their friend, Jimmy Mackintosh?
3) What is a rustler? Can you think of another word, or words, for rustler?
4) Why doesn't Alison's dad use the shotgun on the man?
5) What ideas does Alison have for helping?
6) Why does Alison feel dizzy and sick?
7) Alison tells the police the thieves can't get away until morning. What has she done?

Things to think about

- Neep-heid is a nickname for somebody who isn't thinking. Can you come up with a list of nicknames (friendly ones!) used in your school to describe how people act?
- In the olden days, sheep-stealers used to be killed! Why do you think it was seen as such a bad crime?
- How do you think the thieves felt when the police turned up? Write that part of the story.

Race Against Time
by Michael Coleman

Summary

Colin has arranged to go fishing with Oggie. His friend is usually late. But this time when Colin gets to their meeting place, Oggie has been and gone leaving a strange note behind. Colin follows their usual trail. At first, Oggie's tyre tracks are

clear. Then they get fainter, and are joined by two different footprints. There was a report about an escaped criminal on the news. Could he have anything to do with it? When Colin finds Oggie's abandoned bike he's certain his friend is in terrible trouble. He runs on down to the lake. Suddenly, somebody shouts. And starts chasing him . . .

Questions

1) At what time had the boys said they would meet?
2) What kind of bike does Colin have?
3) Why does Colin's last idea about what Oggie's note says make him nervous?
4) What makes Colin think that Oggie's not alone?
5) Why does Colin think it is his fault that Oggie is missing?
6) How does Oggie explain all the things Colin found?
7) Who really was late – and why?

Things to think about

- This story is set in a country park. Could it have been set in a town? If not, why not?
- The title of any book should match its story in some way. Can you invent another title for this story with the word 'time' in it?
- How do you think the story would have changed if Oggie really had been captured by an escaped prisoner? Write about his rescue.

The A1 Scam
by Bette Paul

Summary

Greg is working at his dad's cafe.
He serves two men whose trailer
is in the car park. He then goes
outside to feed Bruno, his dog. Seeing
the men's trailer, he goes to look at the
logo on its side – and is kidnapped!
He has disturbed crooks who plan to steal
the men's trailer and its load of drugs. They
drive off, taking Greg to a lonely airfield.
There they put the load into another
van they've stolen. Leaving
Greg locked in the trailer, they
escape. But Sharon, Greg's girlfriend,
believes that Bruno knows where Greg is. She follows the dog and Greg is saved.

Questions

1) What does the 'A1' refer to in the title of this book?
2) What logo does Greg see on two men's jackets and a key ring?
3) Why is Greg's dog, Bruno, tied up?
4) What does Greg recognise in the hangar?
5) How does Greg get the trailer shutter open?
6) Why can't Greg hear Sharon when she shouts for him?
7) Why doesn't Greg think the thieves will get very far?

Things to think about

- This story is told by moving from the cafe to the airfield and back again.
  Why is it the best way of telling this particular story?
- This book talks about a logo. Draw the logo described. Can you find any
  other logos – in the yellow pages telephone directory, for instance?
- A logo is often a picture made out of letters. Can you make a logo out of
  your initials?

The Coward
by Helen McCann

Summary

Peter wonders if his father is a coward, like his friend Janeck says. Why is he just a farmer? Why isn't he a soldier, fighting in the war? Then, on his way home from school, Peter finds a wounded man in a ditch. He is looking for the leader of the Freedom Fighters. He has an important list of names to give him. The enemy must not get hold of it. Peter smuggles the list past some guards. He takes it home. Only then does he find out the real truth about his father.

Questions

1) Where were most of the men from Peter's village?
2) What are the enemy soldiers looking for?
3) The man Peter finds in the ditch says his leg is shattered. Think of another word for shattered.
4) Why is the name at the top of the man's list the most important?
5) How does the author tell us that Peter is nervous all the time he is being questioned?
6) How does Peter keep the man's list hidden from the soldiers?
7) Whose name is at the top of the list?

Things to think about

- At the end of the story, Peter knows that his father isn't a coward but he must keep it a secret. Write about Peter's next meeting with Janeck.
- Is being scared the same as being a coward?
- Look at today's newspaper. Can you find an example of a person who you think has acted bravely?

© **LDA** Thrilling Comprehension

The Token
by Elaine Sishton

Summary

A greedy girl is on a train. Two men get on as well. They start talking about a lucky token one of them is wearing round his neck. This man says that the token is magic. It will grant its owner one wish, but that wish must not be for money. Suddenly the man is taken ill and his friend runs for help. The girl steals the token and goes to another seat on the train. But she is so greedy, all she can think of is to wish for money . . .

Questions

1) The girl in this story thinks only of herself. Can you give two examples from pages 1 to 3 to show how the author makes this clear?
2) What did the girl often do to get money from people?
3) How did the girl fool the men into telling the story of the token?
4) What did the writing on the token mean?
5) Why was the ill man lucky?
6) The girl wishes to be surrounded by money. What does the word 'surrounded' mean?
7) How is the girl's wish granted?

 ## *Things to think about*

- Do you feel sorry for the girl? Why or why not?
- If the token had been given to you, what would you have wished for?
- Your wish has been granted! Write a diary to describe what happens to you in the week that follows.

Notes to the Teacher

Answers to the questions in this book are given below. On occasions where a question requires pupils to think creatively and subjectively, you will find the words, 'Each child may answer differently.'

The final three questions on each page are solely intended to stimulate reflective thinking and creative writing, so no answers have been given.

The answers below are in note form and are offered as an instant reference for the teacher, not as a prescription for the exact wording pupils should use. The appropriateness of sentence structure and wording is left to the discretion of the teacher.

ANSWERS

FIVE MINUTE THRILLERS

Flight 901
1) Buy a ticket for Miami. 2) 8:29. 3) Each child may answer differently. 4) Kathy.
5) His own daughter and her rag doll. 6) By going through the Emergency Exit.
7) Each child may answer differently.

Someone at the door
1) Karen's. 2) Because of two killings in their neighbourhood. 3) He worked at a hardware shop. 4) A few minutes. 5) To come back some other time to see if Karen wants to buy his newspaper. She agrees. 6) To tell her that the murderer pretends to be a newspaper salesman. 7) She has already gone to answer the door.

The Playmate
1) Their flat is too small and the food would cost too much. 2) Abandoned, dark and damp. 3) Water sometimes floods in. 4) Each child may answer differently.
5) A human bone. 6) By saying he would stay at home more if he had a pet. 7) A dog.

A Matter of Time
1) March 24, 1738. 2) No. 3) They were getting older. 4) Three times.
5) She has died. 6) To help him to die. 7) Gives him sugar pills.

The Arsonist
1) At a party. 2) To set fire to things. 3) By placing firecrackers in the rubbish near the fuse box. 4) She watches the fire from her car. 5) People were standing in the street pointing at something.
6) Put out the fire with a hose. 7) The £50,000 Mr Fry had given her.

The Hitchhiker.
1) It makes her feel lonely. 2) Because he made mountains out of molehills.
3) She is a woman. 4) That the hitchhiker is a murderer. 5) In the glove compartment.
6) The news that the murderer has been caught. 7) Drops it on the floor.

A Time to Remember
1) It is warm and comfortable. 2) He fainted. 3) He didn't speak or behave like them and his eyes didn't have a hard look. 4) A large house and the name 'Hobbs'.
5) Sad. 6) When he remembers who he is he wants to kill again.
7) He's an expert at helping people get their memory back.

49. Impact-Resistant Glasses Lenses
    1b   2c   3b   4b
50. Embroidery
    1b   2b   3c   4b

Chon

1) It is cheaper to rent a house there. 2) Spend the day outside. 3) A bird.
4) A flying lizard. 5) Diamonds. 6) It is much bigger. 7) To get the gold and diamonds.

Friday Afternoon

1) A bus. 2) Each child may answer differently. 3) He is the only the who hears the newsflash. 4) A nuclear attack. 5) They had argued the last time they were together.
6) "I love you Dad." 7) The missile exploding.

Princess

1) Through the window. 2) A small wooden clock. 3) A cocker spaniel dog. 4) Money.
5) The door is locked with a chain, the thumping noises she makes are very loud, the man pauses before saying she is a dog, and what breed. 6) More money. 7) He is killed.

The Birthday Present

1) They don't have much money. 2) It is rusty and the stuffing is coming out of the seats.
3) A cat. 4) A wish. 5) To bake John a birthday cake. 6) Worthless and helpless.
7) John can have his job back.

The Blue Club

1) Students.   2) To meet people.   3) Philip and Val.   4) Getting ready for the invasion.
5) Snap his fingers.   6) Leave the club.   7) Each child may answer differently.

The Everett Eyes

1) Scared. 2) English. 3) He is an alien. 4) Just before they are 18. It lasts a month.
5) It's very close to exams and he'll miss the school disco.   6) He screams.
7) Cameron, by his special powers.

The Fancy Dress Party

1) 13th floor of an office building. 2) Fancy dress. 3) He isn't in fancy dress.
4) The devil.   5) Mike put a stolen watch in his pocket.   6) He had broken off their engagement to marry someone with more money.   7) Each child may answer differently.

The Look-alike

1) Ron 'Baby' Love. 2) That he mixes with criminals. 3) A girl's menu.
4) A thick set man in a suit.   5) He doesn't want to sign any more autographs.
6) The man who gave him the pen.   7) He signed the autograph.

The Specialist

1) Alvin. 2) Dr A. Lucard.   3) The receptionist and an older man.
4) They both have long canine teeth.   5) It is as cold as ice.
6) That they look like vampires.   7) Each child may answer differently

TEN MINUTE THRILLERS

Grounds for Suspicion

1) Woodside Cottage.
2) Mystery at Woodside, Woodside Kidnappings, Nightmare in November.
3) A sour face, damp with sweat, hollow cheeks, pinball eyes and thin, twisting lips.
4) Murdered his wife. 5) A freshly dug patch of earth. 6) Mr Stone took his prize roses with him. 7) The small button from Mrs Stone's cardigan. Yes it would.

I Dare You

1) Tim and Pete. 2) DANGER - KEEP OUT 3) Each child may answer differently.
4) It is falling to bits. 5) The ghost. 6) He has the kind of face that anybody could trust. 7) He was not at all wet even though he had been out in the rain.

Dead Lucky

1) Tall and thin, pale skin and blue watery eyes. Yes.   2) Friendly and polite. No.

3) Each child may answer differently.   4) Long scratch marks on the victims' bodies.

5) Nice and friendly. No.   6) Her long nails. Page 27, first paragraph.

7) Marion, because of the scratch marks on the bodies.

Knockdown Row

1) Jubilee Row.   2) Each child may answer differently.   3) Southend Pier.

4) The shelves are bare and there are boxes and cases everywhere.

5) She has had a heart attack. No he doesn't care.

6) There is no catch on the outside and the door is too strong for him to break down.

7) He will be crushed when the house is knocked down.

Monkey Business

1) Mrs Jackson who lives in Green Lane.   2) She had been kidnapped.

3) Each child may answer differently.   4) She sees a body on the back seat. The colour of the car is the same as the one in the film.   5) She pretends the torch is broken.

6) He flashes his headlights.   7) A gorilla costume.

Neep-Heid

1) Turnip-head   2) Got him some barbed wire.

3) An animal thief. Each child may answer differently.   4) To keep Alison safe.

5) To tangle barbed wire round the wheels of the van. To unhook the trailor and follow in Dad's car. To wait where she is until Dad left.   6) Because of the bang on her head.

7) She put turnips up their cars' exhaust pipes and in their vans.

Race Against Time

1) 7.00 a.m.   2) A mountain bike.   3) It might refer to an escaped prisoner.

4) The second footprint .   5) Because he kept telling Oggie he is always late.

6) The two footprints were due to Oggie having odd shoes on. He had to hide his bike because he had a punture and had used all his glue to stick the note up.

7) Colin, because he had forgotten to change his watch.

The A1 Scam

1) The road.   2) LNA   3) To stop him going into the cafe.

4) The van from Froggatt's farm   5) By pushing his pencil along the bottom of the shutter.

6) He has fainted.   7) The van has got an oil leak.

The Coward

1) Away fighting.   2) A spy.   3) Each child may answer differently.   4) He is the leader of the network.   5) His face grew red, his heart beat faster, his fingers were clumsy.

6) He puts it inside the wrapper of his chocolate bar.   7) His father's.

The Token

1) She rubs her mother's kiss from her face and doesn't wave to her, she bullies younger children at school.   2) She would lie about her parents splitting up and pretend to cry.

3) She pretended to be asleep.   4) That the holder of the token could be granted one thing - but not money.   5) There was a doctor in the next compartment.

6) Each child may answer differently.   7) She is trapped inside the token.

© LDA Thrilling Comprehension